This book belongs to

_____

Dedicated to

Lola Willow

A B to Jay-Z

By Jessica Chiha

Illustrations by Alex Lehours

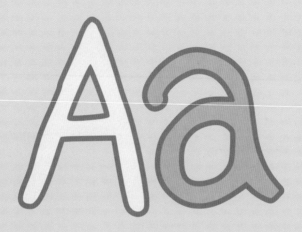

is for

Akon

and you already know he wants to love you

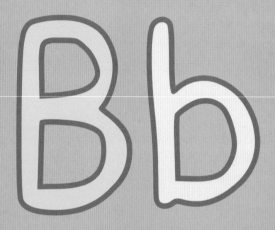

is for

Biggie Smalls

and he loves it when you call him Big Poppa

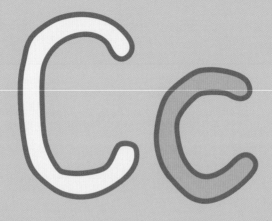

is for

Coolio

and he is living in a gangsta's paradise

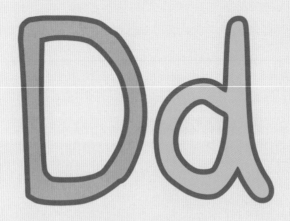

is for

Dr. Dre

and he brought you the Eazy-E's, Ice Cubes and the Snoop D-O-double-G's

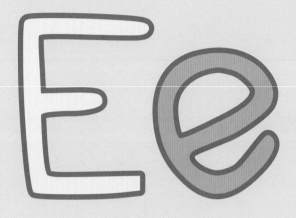

is for

Eazy E

and he's cruising down the street in his 6 4

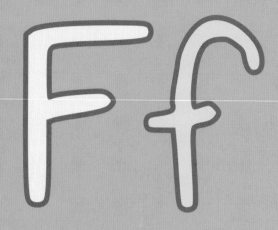

is for

Fifty Cent

and he's going to party like it's your birthday

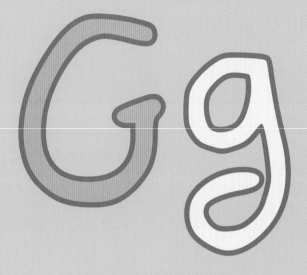

is for

The Game

and he brought you all of his dreams

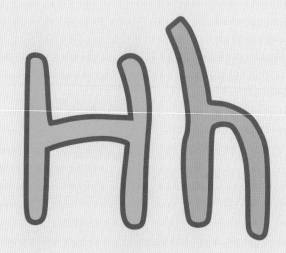

is for

MC Hammer

and he loves hammer time

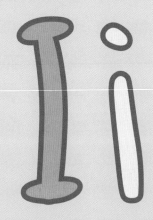

is for

Ice Cube

and his favourite day is Friday

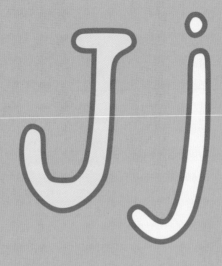

is for

J Cole

and he wants to see you work out

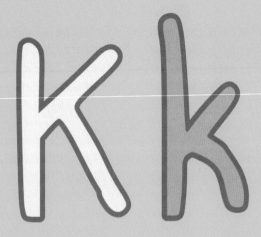

is for

Kendrick Lamar

and he's got a swimming pool that he is ready to dive
into

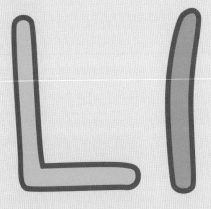

is for

LL Cool J

and he's going back to Cali

is for

Marshall Mathers

and he's the real Slim Shady

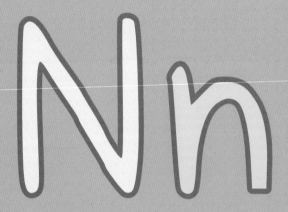

is for

NAS

and he rules the world

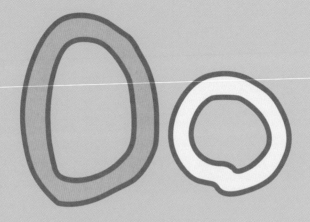

is for

Outkast

and they like to shake it like a polaroid picture

is for

Pharrell

and he's clapping along because he's happy

is for

Queen B (Beyonce)

and she woke up like this

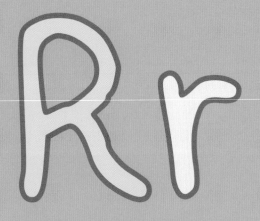

is for

Run DMC

and they think its tricky to rock a rhyme on time

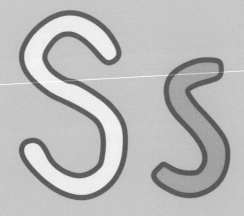

is for

Snoop Dogg

and he's laid back, sipping on orange juice

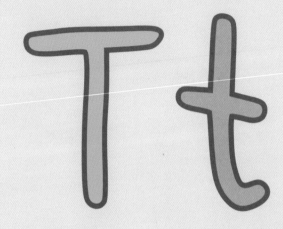

is for

Tupac

and he won't deny it he's a straight rider

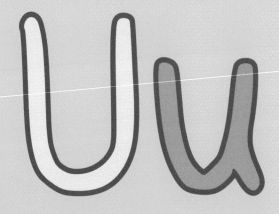

is for

Usher

and he wants you to put your hands up and bend
your knees

is for

Vanilla Ice

and he wants you to stop, collaborate and listen

is for

Lil Wayne

and he's got that young money cash money

is for

Xzibit

and he will pimp your ride

is for

yeezy

and he isn't messing with any gold diggers

is for

Jay Z

and he has 99 problems, but his ABCs ain't one